The Flattered Flying Fish

Illustrated by
E. H. SHEPARD

The Flattered
Flying Fish

AND OTHER POEMS

E. V. RIEU

E. P. DUTTON & COMPANY, INC., NEW YORK

First published in the U.S.A., 1962 by E. P. Dutton & Co., Inc.
Copyright, ©, 1962 by E .V. Rieu
All rights reserved. Printed in the U.S.A.

Second Printing November 1966

Library of Congress Catalog Card Number: 62-18691

Contents

Preface

The poems here collected are the products of my most serious efforts during some thirty years which were otherwise devoted to the lighter task of translating the classics. They are a mixed bag and I have not arranged them in chronological order. Many of them first saw the light of day in *Cuckoo Calling* (Methuen, 1933); and, of these, many have reappeared, in the course of the years, in various anthologies and magazines. Some have been set to music and a number have been broadcast in Great Britain, Canada, Australia and New Zealand. Many, again, with fresh additions, were included in *A Puffin Quartet of Poets* (Penguin Books, 1958). A few have been published so far only in periodicals; and finally a number will here present themselves, in trembling hope, for the first time to an astonished world.

E.V.R.

Highgate, 1962

The Flattered Flying Fish

Soliloquy of a Tortoise
on Revisiting
the Lettuce Beds
after an Interval of One Hour
while supposed
to be
Sleeping
in a Clump
of Blue Hollyhocks

One cannot have enough
Of this delicious stuff!

The Flattered Flying Fish

Said the Shark to the Flying Fish over the phone:
'Will you join me tonight? I am dining alone.
Let me order a nice little dinner for two!
And come as you are, in your shimmering blue.'

Said the Flying Fish: 'Fancy remembering me,
And the dress that I wore at the Porpoises' tea!'
'How could I forget?' said the Shark in his guile:
'I expect you at eight!' and rang off with a smile.

She has powdered her nose; she has put on her things;
She is off with one flap of her luminous wings.
O little one, lovely, light-hearted and vain,
The Moon will not shine on your beauty again!

Hall and Knight

or

$$z+b+x = y+b+z$$

When he was young his cousins used to say of Mr Knight:
'This boy will write an Algebra – or looks as if he might.'
And sure enough, when Mr Knight had grown to be a man,
He purchased pen and paper and an inkpot, and began.

But he very soon discovered that he couldn't write at all,
And his heart was filled with yearnings for a certain Mr
    Hall;
Till, after many years of doubt, he sent his friend a card:
'Have tried to write an Algebra, but find it very hard.'

Now Mr Hall himself had tried to write a book for schools,
But suffered from a handicap: he didn't know the rules.
So when he heard from Mr Knight and understood his gist,
He answered him by telegram: 'Delighted to assist.'

So Mr Hall and Mr Knight they took a house together,
And they worked away at algebra in any kind of weather,
Determined not to give it up until they had evolved
A problem so constructed that it never could be solved.

'How hard it is,' said Mr Knight, 'to hide the fact from
        youth
That x and y are equal: it is such an obvious truth!'
'It is,' said Mr Hall, 'but if we gave a b to each,
We'd put the problem well beyond our little victims' reach.

Or are you anxious, Mr Knight, lest any boy should see
The utter superfluity of this repeated *b*?'
'I scarcely fear it,' he replied, and scratched his grizzled
      head,
'But perhaps it *would* be safer if to *b* we added *z*.'

'A brilliant stroke!' said Hall, and added *z* to either side;
Then looked at his accomplice with a flush of happy pride.
And Knight, he winked at Hall (a very pardonable lapse).
And they printed off the Algebra and sold it to the chaps.

The Snake and the Snake-Charmer

'Sing me to sleep,
    Light of me eyes!'
'Charmed!' said the Charmer,
    Wary and wise.

Classical airs,
    Handel and Brahms,
Anger the snake.
    So do the Psalms.

Sullivan's songs
    Over-excite;
Rachmaninoff
    Ends in a bite.

None but a jazz
    Melody charms
Flickering eyes
    Full of alarms.

Flickering eyes
    Drowsily close.
Odours of Ind
    Enter his nose —

Odours of India
Deep in the tune,
India perfumed
Under the noon.

The White Rabbit

He is white as Helvellyn when winter is well in;
   His whiskers are mobile and tender.
If it weren't for the greed that compels him to feed
   Without ceasing, his form would be slender.

With elegant hops he crushes or crops
   All the flowers that bloom in the garden;
Yet such is the grace that suffuses his face,
   He wins, without asking, our pardon.

The Sun, who rides heaven from Dover to Devon
   Inspecting furred folk and their habits,
Breaks out into poesy: 'What summer snow is he
   Made of, this pearl among rabbits?'

And at night on the lawn as he waits for the dawn,
   Rapt in dreams of a rabbit's perfection,
The Moon in her stride sweeps the cloudlets aside
   To rejoice in his silver reflection.

Peter and Percival
or
The Penguins' Revolt

I

THE SUITORS

Peter and Percival lived in a place
Where the cold is too bitter for People to face,
But Peter and Percival both had contrived
To be Penguins, not People – and so they survived.

In their frozen abode at Antarctica's end
They not only flourished, but each had a friend;
For Fate, having made up her mind to be merciful,
Gave Percy to Peter and Peter to Percival.

Now Perce was a poet, a moulder of metre,
While prose was the medium chosen by Peter;
Yet Peter delighted in Percival's verse
And the prose of his Pete was as music to Perce.

This master of prose and this maker of rhyme
Adored the same lady, and both at a time;
For each, in his fashion, aspired to the hand
Of the Queen of the Penguins in Enderby Land.

When Peter and Perce were received at the Court,
Peter's proposal was painfully short,
For all he could say in the Presence was 'Yum!'
And it might have been better if he had been dumb.

Percy was equally wanting in tact,
Though endowed with the eloquence Peter had lacked;
For without having studied Her Majesty's views
He gaily committed himself to the Muse.

'What plumage!' he sang. 'What a beak! What a leg!
To think that such beauty came out of an egg!'
And he stopped for applause – in a silence complete
But for one little loyal explosion from Pete.

Her Majesty looked at the pair with a frown,
And remarked, as she primly adjusted her crown:
'Peter is pitiful; Percival worse:
We never have heard such indelicate verse!

'Be off with you both, to discover the Pole.
And polish your style on the way to your goal,
Till Percy has learnt to add reason to rhyme,
And Pete to use more than a word at a time.'

Not a murmur from Pete, not a stanza from Percy,
No sighs of regret and no sueing for mercy,
But flipper in flipper they passed from her sight
Out under the stars of the Antarctic night.

II

THE REBELS

They had waddled a dismal disconsolate week
Before Percy recovered the use of his beak.
He blinked at the desolate acres of snow,
And moaned in his misery: 'Oh, what a go!'

'Is it sense,' he complained, 'is it fair, is it nice
To be banished for love over hummocky ice?
O Peterkin, Peter, have *you* any hope
Of Polar Discoveries?' Peter said: 'Nope!'

'And what if we penetrate into the South?
Is there anything there to put into one's mouth?
I once was a poet: at present I wish
For nothing so much as a – ' Peter said: 'Fish.'

'How apt! How concise! How deliciously put!'
Said Percival, scratching his head with his foot.
And he pondered a moment before he expressed
The emotions that flooded his feathery breast.

'I would like to be loyal, but since we were banished
My love for Her Majesty seems to have vanished.
I used to be charmed by her perfume and paint,
But just at the moment – ' Said Peter: 'You ain't.'

'How perfect the pleasures of amity are!'
Said Perce, with his eye on a southerly star.
And they walked for a little, preoccupied each
With thoughts that refused to be put into speech.

'I observe you are ready,' said Perce, 'to rebel,'
When a hiccough from Peter had broken the spell.
'And if you are ready, then why should we wait?
Let us found a Reformed and Republican State!

'With freedom to live as we jolly well please,
Freedom to hiccough, and freedom to sneeze,
Freedom for Poetry, freedom for Prose –
Let us dance the Democracy in with our toes!'

So they tripped in their glee through the star-spangled
Penguins in harmony, utterly right;   [night,
While the silent Aurora went flickering forth
And shivered the sky from the South to the North.

They danced their delight, in the star-sprinkled weather,
Peter and Percival, birds of a feather;
And the awful Aurora with shimmering hands
Shook her curtain out over the ice-covered lands.

What Does it Matter?

What does it matter to you and me
Whether it's half past eight or three?
The nursery clock has just gone one;
And hark, the clock in the hall's begun!
But it must be wrong, for it's striking seven;
And there goes another one, on to eleven!
      And I think it's four,
      But it might be more –
Oh, what does it matter to you and me?
Let's have dinner and call it tea!
And we'll all go to bed and wake at three,
  For the Sun will be right in the morning.

Two People

Two people live in Rosamund,
  And one is very nice;
The other is devoted
  To every kind of vice —

To walking where the puddles are,
  And eating far too quick,
And saying words she shouldn't know,
  And wanting spoons to lick.

Two people live in Rosamund,
  And one (I say it twice)
Is very nice *and* very good:
  The other's only nice.

Arethusa

Arethusa the gay is departed
  From the school where the porpoises play,
Arethusa the maiden light-hearted,
  In her suit of unshrinkable grey;
Arethusa the dainty and dapper;
  No diver so daring as she;
Arethusa the liveliest flapper
  That ever swam over the sea.

Arethusa, Althea and Io,
  Sea-sisters, were swimming as one,
A finny and frolicsome trio,
  In the light of the westering sun.
At sunset together they sported –
  When the names were called over at dawn,
Althea and Io reported,
  But the gay Arethusa was gone.

Was she lured to the open Atlantic
  By the dancing and lights on a boat,
Or the sound of the mighty Megantic
  With its deep and reverberant note?
Did the Moon's irresponsible crescent
  Bemuse her to swim in her sleep,
Or a monster with face phosphorescent
  Come up at her out of the deep?

She forgot how to ride the white horses
    And canter the watery plain;
She forgot how the stars in their courses
    Guide porpoises over the main.
She wandered in every direction
    Through Ocean's unharvested ways;
She lost her school-porpoise complexion,
    And snorted in desolate bays.

'What a voice!' said the Cod to the Flounder.
    'What a wholly regrettable din!'
But the Pilot-Fish paused when he found her,
    In spite of the haste he was in;
And to seas where the weather is finer,
    And parts where her relatives go,
Like a little tug handling a liner,
    He took Arethusa in tow.

The Lost Cat

She took a last and simple meal when there were none to
     see her steal –
    A jug of cream upon the shelf, a fish prepared for
     dinner;
And now she walks a distant street with delicately sandalled
     feet,
    And no one gives her much to eat or weeps to see her
     thinner.

O my belovèd come again, come back in joy, come back in
     pain,
    To end our searching with a mew, or with a purr our
     grieving;
And you shall have for lunch or tea whatever fish swim in
     the sea
    And all the cream that's meant for me – and not a word
     of thieving!

Portrait of a House

The house that we live in was built in a place
That was once a mere cube of unoccupied space;
And the birds that flew through it and passed on their way
Would collide with a wall or a window today.

The rooms in the house are of medium size,
The sort that an ant would regard with surprise;
While a whale could express no opinion at all,
For his bulk would prevent him from passing the hall.

The stairs are arranged with such exquisite skill
That a person can climb or descend them at will;
And the absence of rain from the attics is proof
That the architect thought of supplying a roof.

Of the doors and the windows our only complaint
Is the fact that you can't see the wood for the paint:
A trouble with which we've decided to deal
By allowing the paint to continue to peel.

The chairs and the tables are perfectly tame,
And to speak of them harshly is rather a shame;
But nevertheless I am bound to remark
On their savage resistance when bumped in the dark.

In the kitchen, in spite of its tropical clime,
Two cats and a cook spend the whole of their time.
The cats have been known to meander about,
But the cook is a fixture and never goes out.

It is said that mysterious sounds may be heard
In the house when it's empty; but this is absurd.
If you've gone there to listen, it's clear to a dunce
That the house will have ceased to be empty at once.

We've a spare-room prepared for the casual guest,
But it really is not what the name would suggest;
For although it's a room, it is never to spare,
As someone or other is constantly there.

I have made it quite clear that our chosen abode
Is different from all of the rest in the road –
What a beautiful house for play, dinner and slumber!
And yet to the postman it's only a number.

The Lesser Lynx

The laughter of the Lesser Lynx
   Is often insincere:
It pays to be polite, he thinks,
   If Royalty is near.

So when the Lion steals his food
   Or kicks him from behind,
He smiles, of course – but oh, the rude
   Remarks that cross his mind!

Ode to Duty

Oh it's pleasant when dinner is done
    To feel that the fun
    Has scarcely begun,
And to spend half an hour at the sink;
    But it's pleasanter still,
    Though less of a thrill,
To sit and do nothing but think.

And it's healthy (or so it is said)
    Not to linger in bed,
    But to get up instead
And tackle the work of the day;
    But it's pleasanter still
    To pretend to be ill
Till somebody comes with a tray.

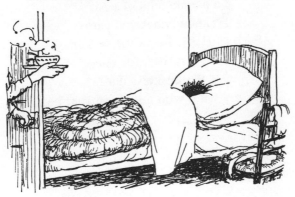

Oh it's nice, and might possibly pay,
　　To dig in the clay
　　From October to May
In the hope that a cabbage will rise;
　　But it's pleasanter still,
　　In spite of the bill,
To rely on the phone for supplies.

And it's helpful to bring in the coal –
　　Indeed, on the whole,
　　I envy the soul
Who approaches the job as a pleasure;
　　But not being such
　　I prefer very much
To fall back on the aid of a Treasure.

It's polite to send in a Return
　　To people who yearn
　　To know what you earn,
Such as H.M. Inspector of Taxes;
　　But I'd rather, for one,
　　Get the business done
By my wife, who knows all that he axes.

Yes, it's pleasant to do as one should,
    And I'm sure that I would,
    If only I could;
But I wish it to be understood
    That it's pleasanter still,
    By an effort of will,
To let other people be good.

Tony the Turtle

Tony was a Turtle
  Very much at ease,
Swimming in the sunshine
  Through the summer seas,
And feeding on the fishes
Irrespective of their wishes,
With a 'By your leave' and 'Thank you'
  And a gentlemanly squeeze.

Tony was a Turtle
  Who loved a civil phrase;
Anxious and obliging,
  Sensitive to praise.
And to hint that he was snappy
Made him thoroughly unhappy;
For Tony was a Turtle
  With most engaging ways.

Tony was a Turtle
  Who thought, before he fed,
Of other people's comfort,
  And as he ate them said;
'If I seem a little grumpy,
It is *not* that you are lumpy.'
  For Tony was a Turtle
  Delicately bred.

The Happy Hedgehog

The happiness of hedgehogs
　Lies in complete repose.
They spend the months of winter
　In a long delicious doze;
And if they note the time at all
　They think 'How fast it goes!'

The Tortoise and the Magistrate

A Tortoise ambling down the Strand
  On window-shopping bent
Was stopped by a policeman's hand
  For loitering with intent.
'Or failing that,' the Bobby said,
  'For dashing slowly through
The traffic when the light was red –
  A shocking thing to do.
For folk who won't keep on the go
  The Strand is clearly no street;
And that,' he ended, 'being so,
  You come with me to Bow Street.'

The Tortoise shed a tear or two
    In her surprise and pain
She had meant to get to Waterloo
    And catch an early train
That would enable her (or might
    If it were not held up)
To kiss her little ones good-night
    And presently to sup.
Instead of which, at four o'clock,
    She found to her distress
That she was standing in the dock,
    Surrounded by the Press.

The Magistrate who heard the case
    Looked sternly at the Copper.
'Your zeal,' he said, 'was out of place;
    Your conduct most improper.

This quiet, unassuming dame,
  Whom *you* took for a slattern,
Puts you and all of us to shame
  And sets the world a pattern.
Speed does not always win the race
  Or even get you there.
Look up that celebrated chase:
  The Tortoise v. the Hare.'

Then, smiling at the fair accused,
  He said, 'Dry up your tears.
However badly you were used,
  You now need have no fears.
So go in peace. You leave this place,
  A credit to the nation
With no stain on your carapace –
  I mean your reputation.
You still have time, at Waterloo,
  To catch the 7:01.
And I need hardly say to *you*,
  Don't break into a run.'

The Children's Lament

(WITH THANKS TO
ALGERNON CHARLES SWINBURNE)

We are tired of Rome and Sparta,
   And Hereward the Wake;
Of John and Magna Charta
   (What difference does it make?);
Of circumnavigations;
   Sums, angles and equations;
Of Latin conjugations
   And verbs, and what they take.

We may not eat at table
   Whatever there may be,
Nor all that we are able,
   Nor everything we see;
They watch the butter taken,
And sugar-castors shaken;
We are not sure of bacon,
   And jam is never free.

Of something rich and tasty
   That is not made with rice,
A pudding or a pasty
   Unusually nice,

No smile, however grateful,
   Ensures a second plateful;
Yet sago, though it's hateful,
   Is often offered twice.

They do not think it funny
   To break a window-pane:
They talk of fines and money
   And letting in the rain;
And when we make grimaces
At men in public places,
However good the face is,
   Our labour is in vain.

When bed is most delicious
   And we could sleep all day,
We rise, because they wish us;
   But when *their* dinner tray
Comes, with hot soup to swallow,
And lovely things to follow,
Though we feel faint and hollow,
   'Goodnight' is all they say.

The Paint Box

'Cobalt and umber and ultramarine,
Ivory black and emerald green –
What shall I paint to give pleasure to you?'
'Paint for me somebody utterly new.'

'I have painted you tigers in crimson and white.'
'The colours were good and you painted aright.'
'I have painted the cook and a camel in blue
And a panther in purple.' 'You painted them true.

'Now mix me a colour that nobody knows,
And paint me a country where nobody goes.
And put in it people a little like you,
Watching a unicorn drinking the dew.'

Dirge for a Bad Boy

Richard has been sent to bed:
Let a solemn dirge be said.
Sent to bed before his time,
Sentenced for a nursery crime.
Draw down the blinds in every room
And fill the dismal house with gloom.
Richard has been sent to bed:
Let a solemn dirge be said.

Tell the cat and kitten they
Must cease from their unseemly play.
Stop the telephone from ringing;
Stop the kettle from its singing.
And hark, is that the Hoover's hum?
Let the Hoover too be dumb.
Richard has been sent to bed:
Let a solemn dirge be said.

Turn off, turn off, the central heat,
And let the cold creep round our feet.
Put out the fire and let it die
Underneath that juicy pie,
That we may eat (if eat we must)
Cold apple and a colder crust.
Richard has been sent to bed:
Let a solemn dirge be said.

And when the time has come for all
To follow through the darkened hall,
Let every sound of mirth be banned –
Take each a candle in his hand,
And winding up the stairway slow
In melancholy order go,
While this solemn dirge is said
For a poor sinner in his bed.

Lullaby for a Naughty Girl

Oh peace, my Penelope: slaps are the fate
Of all little girls who are born to be great;
And the greatest of Queens have all been little girls
And dried up their tears on their kerchiefs or curls.

Oh sleep: and your heart that has sobbed for so long
Will mend and grow merry and wake you to song;
For the world is a lovelier place than it seems,
And a smack cannot follow you into your dreams.

The dark Cleopatra was slapped on the head,
And she wept as she lay in her great golden bed;
But the dark Cleopatra woke up with a smile
As she thought of the little boats out on the Nile.

And Helen of Troy had many a smack:
She moaned and she murmured the Greek for 'Alack!'
But the sun rose in Argos, and wonderful joy
Came with the morning to Helen of Troy.

They sent Guinevere without supper to sleep
In her grey little room at the top of the Keep;
And the stars over Camelot waited and wept
Till the peeping moon told them that Guinevere slept.

There was grief in Castile and dismay in Madrid
When they slapped Isabella for something she did;
But she slept — and could laugh in the morning again
At the Dons of Castile, the Hidalgos of Spain.

And oh, how Elizabeth cried in her cot
When she wanted her doll and her Nanny said not!
But the sparrows awoke and the summer sun rose,
And there was the doll on the bed by her toes!

So sleep, my Penelope: slaps are the fate
Of all little girls who are born to be great;
But the world is a lovelier place than it seems,
And a smack cannot follow you into your dreams.

A Bad Day by the River

The Overlord of Roaches
   Has made a Royal Rule
For Roach and Rudd and Loaches,
   And fish of pond and pool;

Proclaimed it in the river
  And nailed it to a tree:
That no fish whatsoever
  Is to be caught by me –

Signed by the King of Roaches
  In this, his Royal Stream;
Sealed by the Lord of Loaches;
  Attested by a Bream;
Engrossed by twenty Perches;
  Translated into French;
Read out in all the churches,
  And broadcast by a Tench.

The Revoke

The Lion finds it difficult to get a game of cards
Since that unfortunate affair at Mrs Leo Pard's.
In vain he rings his hostess up in accents kind and hearty –
'They much regret . . . they cannot come . . . they have
    another party.'

Perhaps he *had* been hasty – he was certainly provoked
When his dainty little partner, Lady Antelope, revoked.
The Lion smiled and licked his chops in reminiscent vein –
'I'll wait till supper is announced, *if* I am asked again!'

Sir Smasham Uppe

Good afternoon, Sir Smasham Uppe!
We're having tea: do take a cup.
Sugar and milk? Now let me see –
Two lumps, I think? . . . Good gracious me!
The silly thing slipped off your knee!
Pray don't apologize, old chap:
A very trivial mishap!
So clumsy of you? How absurd!
My dear Sir Smasham, not a word!
Now do sit down and have another,
And tell us all about your brother –
You know, the one who broke his head.
Is the poor fellow still in bed? –
A chair – allow me, sir! . . . Great Scott!
That *was* a nasty smash! Eh, what?
Oh, not at all: the chair was old –
Queen Anne, or so we have been told.
We've got at least a dozen more:
Just leave the pieces on the floor.
I want you to admire our view:
Come nearer to the window, do;
And look how beautiful . . . Tut, tut!
You didn't see that it was shut?
I hope you are not badly cut!
Not hurt? A fortunate escape!

Amazing! Not a single scrape!
And now, if you have finished tea,
I fancy you might like to see
A little thing or two I've got.
That china plate? Yes, worth a lot:
A beauty too . . . Ah, there it goes!
I trust it didn't hurt your toes?
Your elbow brushed it off the shelf?
Of course: I've done the same myself.
And now, my dear Sir Smasham — Oh,
You surely don't intend to go?
You *must* be off? Well, come again.
So glad you're fond of porcelain!

Night Thought
of a
Tortoise
Suffering from
Insomnia
on a Lawn

The world is very flat –
There is no doubt of that.

A Musical At Home

A little party in the house –
The first to come is Mr Grouse.
And he has hardly settled down
When they announce Sir Fractious Frown;
And, just as talk is getting slack,
My Lord and Lady Answer Back.
This *is* a pleasure: I am proud.
Step in: you'll find we're quite a crowd.
And Mrs Contradict, I see,
Is just behind you: pardon me!
Another ring. Ah Lady Snap,
Permit me to remove your wrap.
How good of you to come so far
And bring the Grumbles in your car! –
Now bless my soul, I know that face!
And yet – of course, it's Miss Grimace.
These fashions alter people so!
Come in and take your hat off. No?
And who's this trotting up the stair?
Little Miss Quarrel, I declare!
So musical, so quick, so merry,
And clever with her fingers – very!
Ah Mr Bump, good afternoon!
I thought we might expect you soon.
Another knock. Dear Major Punch,

Most kind of you to rush your lunch!
Let me present Miss Whack. You've met her?
Old friends, you say? So much the better!
Lord Biff – allow me – Canon Batt.
At school together? Fancy that!
The world is really very small.
Excuse me – someone in the hall.
Aha, the gallant Captain Kick!
Late? Not at all. You're in the nick.
And you, Miss Shindy, come along:
We're counting on you for a song.
And now I think we're nearly done –
All here and happy – but for one.
Ah Mrs Tears, how *do* you do?
So glad you've brought your music too!
What dreadful weather! Do come in.
And now we might as well begin.

Rendez-vous with a Beetle

Meet me in Usk
   And drone to me
Of what a beetle's
   Eye can see
When lamps are lit
And the bats flit
   In Usk
   At dusk.

And tell me if
   A beetle's nose
Detects the perfume
   Of the rose
As gardens fade
And stars invade
   The dusk
   In Usk.

The Albatross and the Equator

'Albatross, Albatross, why do you fly
Under my blue equatorial sky?
Albatross, Albatross, why do you roam
So far from your icy delectable home?'

'Capricorn warned me to turn to the right,
But I strayed from my course in the dead of the night;
And the stars of the tropics, so many and new,
Led me by long ways and weary to you.'

The kindly Equator arose with a yawn
To the green and gold of the tropical dawn.
He called his Leviathans, little and large,
And handed the Albatross into their charge.

And he said to his Porpoises: 'Cease from your play,
And listen to me for the rest of the day:
I never have seen and seldom have heard
Of such an amazingly beautiful bird.

'She has flown from the far impossible South,
And strange are the sounds that come out of her mouth;
But the white of her breast and the spread of her wings
Are both surpassingly wonderful things.'

So they crowned her with seaweed Queen of the Birds
And humbly addressed her with flattering words;
And they gave her oysters and elegant fish
Daintily served on an amethyst dish.

They gave her a coral isle set in the calms
With a long white beach of coconut palms.
'Deign with your delicate feet,' said they,
'To tread this shade in the heat of the day.'

But the Albatross smiled with a tear in her heart,
As she said: 'I will walk for a little apart.'
And she paced by the echoing ocean alone,
Crooning a sorrowful song of her own:

'Fair are the tropical seas in the noon,
And fair in the glistening path of the moon.
But, oh, dearer to me are the storms of the Horn
Where the grey world-wandering waves are born.'

One moment they saw her, the next she had fled
Like a dream in the dawn or a shaft that is sped;
And all that she left on that desolate strand
Was the print of her foot and a tear in the sand.

She flew through the day and she flew through the night
With a heart that was bursting with hope and delight,
As the changing horizons came up with a swing
And the long leagues of ocean slipped under her wing –

Into the far incredible South,
Till she tasted the smell of the snow in her mouth,
And fluttered to rest in the land of her birth
On the ice that envelops the ends of the Earth

Jungle Night Club

There is music in the jungle on the hills of Malabar,
   And the coconuts are swaying
      By the sea;
For the elephant is playing to the dancers near and far
   On the sighing saxophone
   In a sentimental drone —
      Ah me!
While the golden fireflies flutter to the lure of his refrain,
   Mimicking the stars above,
   Dancing to the light of love,
      In and out, in and out,
         Through the rain.

See the melancholy monkey by the solitary palm!
   He has drowned his sense of wrong
   In a bumperful of bhong,
And he ponders life's perplexities in philosophic calm.
      Too long!
   For the bonds of Fate are strong;
   And a flood of sorrows rise
   To his unresisting eyes
As he thinks of his Matilda in the homely cotton-tree,
   Fond and fretting, far away —
      Ah me!

Meditations
of a Tortoise
Dozing under a Rosetree
near a Beehive
at Noon
while
a Dog
scampers about
and a Cuckoo calls
from a
Distant Wood

So far as I can see,
There is no one like me.

The Unicorn

The Unicorn stood, like a king in a dream,
On the bank of a dark Senegambian stream;
And flaming flamingoes flew over his head,
As the African sun rose in purple and red.

Who knows what the thoughts of a unicorn are
When he shines on the world like a visiting star;
When he comes from the magical pages of story
In the pride of his horn and a halo of glory?

He followed the paths where the jungle beasts go,
And he walked with a step that was stately and slow;
But he threw not a shadow and made not a sound,
And his foot was as light as the wind on the ground.

The lion looked up with his terrible eyes,
And growled like the thunder to hide his surprise.
He thought for a while, with a paw in the air;
Then tucked up his tail and turned into his lair.

The gentle giraffe ran away to relate
The news to his tawny and elegant mate,
While the snake slid aside with a venomous hiss,
And the little birds piped: 'There is something amiss!'

But the Unicorn strode with his head in a cloud
And uttered his innocent fancies aloud.
'What a wonderful world!' he was heard to exclaim;
'It is better than books: it is sweeter than fame!'

And he gazed at himself, with a thrill and a quiver,
Reflected in white by the slow-flowing river:
'Oh, speak to me, dark Senegambian stream,
And prove that my beauty is more than a dream!'

He had paused for a word in the midst of his pride,
When a whisper came down through the leaves at his side
From a spying, malevolent imp of an ape
With a twist in his tail and a villainous shape:

'He was made by the stroke of a fanciful pen;
He was wholly invented by ignorant men.
One word in his ear, and one puff of the truth –
And a unicorn fades in the flower of his youth.'

The Unicorn heard, and the demon of doubt
Crept into his heart, and the sun was put out.
He looked in the water, but saw not a gleam
In the slow-flowing deep Senegambian stream.

He turned to the woods, and his shadowy form
Was seen through the trees like the moon in a storm.

And the darkness fell down on the Gambian plain;
And the stars of the Senegal sought him in vain.

He had come like a beautiful melody heard
When the strings of the fiddle are tunefully stirred;
And he passed where the splendours of melody go
When the hand of the fiddler surrenders the bow.

The Lament of the White Mouse

We shared in one delightful house;
    We shared a mossy bed.
I never knew another mouse
    Than her – and she is dead.

The beady eye, the nimble strength,
    The soft and silken fur!
The whiskers, and the noble length
    Of tail that followed her!

And now I'm lonely in the run,
    And lonely on the stair,
And lonely in the nest we spun –
    So warm when she was there!

The wheel she loved to turn is still.
    The feet that ran so light
Have twinkled up the heavenly hill
    And tread the wheel of night.

Cat's Funeral

Bury her deep, down deep,
Safe in the earth's cold keep,
   Bury her deep —

No more to watch bird stir;
No more to clean dark fur;
No more to glisten as silk;
No more to revel in milk;
   No more to purr.

Bury her deep, down deep;
She is beyond warm sleep.
She will not walk in the night;
She will not wake to the light.
   Bury her deep.

Pirate Passes

In the stronghold of his will fighting his last battle still,
  Clothed in all his fallen grandeur Galapago Jimmy lay,
Where they left him as a feast for the jungle fowl and
      beast,
  Fearing yet his eye in anger and the sword that could
      not slay.

And the only sound he heard was the paradisal bird,
　　Perched at ease among the beacons of the blood-red
　　　　forest-flame,
Piping all her heart to him, calling 'Galapago Jim',
　　Turning evil into beauty, making music of his name.

All the night her voice pursued, and she mocked him as
　　　　she wooed
　　Singing 'Galapago Jimmy, join me through the golden
　　　　bars',
When the dark was at its deepest and the way to heaven
　　　　steepest
　　Past the captains and the cohorts and the companies of
　　　　stars.

All the day rang her refrain, till the West was red again,
　　And he smiled a sudden smile, and the soul of him
　　　　slipped by,
As the birds of day were homing in the half-light of the
　　　　gloaming,
　　Past the captains and the cohorts and the armies of the
　　　　sky.

The Green Train

The Blue Train for the South – but the Green Train for us.
Nobody knows when the Green Train departs.
Nobody sees her off. There is no noise; no fuss;
No luggage on the Green Train;
No whistle when she starts.
But quietly at the right time they wave the green light
And she slides past the platform and plunges into the night.

Wonderful people walking down the long Green Train,
As the engine gathers speed.
And voices talking.
'Where does she go to, Guard?'
Where indeed?
But what does it matter
So long as the night is starred?
Who cares for time, and who cares for the place,
So long as the Green Train thunders on into space?

The Whale

A Whale of the cachalot sort
Came up from the depths with a snort,
And lifting his tail like a thundering flail
Belaboured the sea in his sport.
The flying fish shuddered in fright
And the porpoises paled at the sight
Of the foam and commotion he made in the ocean
A league to the left and the right.

A Volcano looked down on the bay
And smoked in a satisfied way:
The fumes of his fire rose up like a spire –
Leviathan paused in his play.
And he said with a watery sigh,
'The monster is greater than I!
How I envy this mountain whose spout is a fountain
That reaches the roof of the sky!'

With a feeling akin to chagrin
He sounded and sank from the scene;
And he killed a great squid (in his anger he did)
With an eye like a porridge tureen.
Then he turned his square nose to the Pole,
His southern and ultimate goal,
And brooding on slaughter he sped through the water
With never a word to a soul.

And he came to the country of ice
And circled the continent twice.
'He is missing his meals,' cried the motherly seals;
  While the penguins were free with advice.
  Till at length upon Enderby Deep,
  Where the snow-laden hurricanes sweep,
With the Antarctic billows for bedding and pillows
  He rocked in a merciful sleep.

  He had slept on his passionate pride
  For the ebb and the flood of a tide,
When a maidenly whale with a tapering tail
  Rose up from the sea at his side.
  She gave him a whimsical look,
  And a touch of her delicate fluke,
And fled from his waking with tender heart quaking
  In fear of rebuff or rebuke.

  But as one who awakes from a swoon
  To the sound of a magical tune
He was caught by the gleam of her silvery beam
  In the diamond light of the moon;
  And from out of the slough of despond,
  To the edge of the sea and beyond,
Where the Aurora lingers with flickering fingers,
  He followed her, foolish and fond.

And he sang her a sea serenade:
'My queen, be no longer afraid.
I will make you a home in the heart of the foam,
  O lovely and lovable maid!'
  And the candles of night were put out
  By Dawn, the dispeller of doubt,
As the maid oceanic, forgetting her panic,
  Replied, with a feathery spout:

  'O Cachalot, king of the blue,
  I will swim with you loyal and true.
In weal or in woe, wheresoever you go,
  I will dive with no other than you.
  Where the Kraken lies secretly curled,
  Where the hissing harpoon may be hurled,
In battle and thunder, above seas or under,
  I am yours to the ends of the world!'

  So he swam by the side of his queen
  Conversing of days that had been,
And he spoke in a gay and a casual way
  Of the *little* volcano he'd seen.
  And she heard with the ghost of a smile,
  But a heart that was empty of guile,
As they journeyed together through fair and foul
        weather,
  By ice-floe and iceberg and isle.

Pirates on Funafuti

Full many a magic island lies within the seas of coral,
But only Funafuti wields a magic that is moral.
There is no island of the East or in the Spanish Main
That boasts a fauna so correct, a flora so urbane.

It is a pretty sight to see the billows doff their caps
In breaking on the beach, though this is natural perhaps.
The very coconuts that grow so slender in the glades
Incline politely to the winds, though these are only trades.

One sunny day a pirate band approached this happy shore,
Fresh from the looting of a ship, and looking out for more —
Jack Slaughter, Galapago Jim, Sam Stiff and Hairy Hugh,
Cuthbert the Cook and Barmy Bill — they *were* an ugly
   crew.

The first on Funafuti, as it fell, was Captain Jack,
Whom Sam in swinging round an oar had landed on his
   back.
And he rose up in the shallows with a murderous
   grimace —
When an unexpected simper altogether changed his face.

'Your pardon, Mr Stiff,' he said, 'for being in the way.
The fault was mine entirely. Not another word, I pray.'

The crew were dumb. 'Be good enough to join me on
    the sand.
Come, Mr Galapago Jim. Allow me, Cook, a hand.'

The crew obeyed. They would have feared an angry lion
    less
Than this perplexing suavity, this painful *politesse*.
But as in turn they disembarked and caught the island's
    spell
Each felt an impulse to behave unusually well.

Said Jim, 'I happen to have brought a change in my
    valise.
Do me the honour, sir, I beg, of slipping into these.'
'Your kindly thought,' the Skipper said, 'may well
    prevent a chill.
Excuse me for a moment.' And he went behind a hill.

And so in all propriety they dined upon the beach,
Restricting their consumption to a single helping each,
And choosing the right cutlery with cultivated ease
For caviare, asparagus, or macaroni cheese.

The evening's pleasure ended with a little tune from
    Sam.
'You cannot think,' the Captain said, 'how deeply moved
    I am.
The moonlit scene, the tender words, my mother's
    favourite song –
I wonder, O my comrades, if a pirate's life is wrong!'

They led him sobbing to his bed, their own tears falling
    fast;
They tucked him in and held his hand until the fit had
    passed;
They smoothed his pillow neatly, put his cutlass under-
    neath,
And in a glass beside him popped his artificial teeth.

Then one by one they said their prayers and folded up
    their clothes,
Forgetful of the ribald jest, the customary oaths;
And with a fairy tale or two they talked themselves
    asleep
To the murmur of the palm-trees and the gently stirring
    deep.

They sailed at dawn. And as they left the magic coast
    behind,
The conduct of the company immediately declined.
Their breakfast was a brutal thing; at lunch they hardly
    spoke;
By dinner-time civility was treated as a joke.

But still on Funafuti beach the ocean rollers break
With a softly silenced thunder, lest the little turtles
    wake;
Clams in their crannies hide their yawns; and everything
    is done
To the perfect satisfaction of the overseeing Sun.

The Princess Priscilla

When the Princess Priscilla goes out
There aren't *any* dragons about:
   The dragons decide
   It is better to hide
While the Princess Priscilla is out.

As the Princess Priscilla goes by
There's a kind of a gleam in her eye –
   The tail of no dragon
   Could possibly wag on
When the Princess Priscilla goes by.

The Missing Cuckoo

This year the cuckoo has not come to us;
Or else a cuckoo came and he was dumb.
Ah, when will our Spring come?

This year the cuckoo has not come to us;
And yet the people say,
Down Essex way,
They have already heard
More than sufficient of the tedious bird;
And there are lots,
According to the news, in Notts;
Whereas in Bucks
Cuckoos are commoner than ducks.
Also there issues from a part of Flint
An ugly hint
That local cuckoos have begun to stutter –
They had so much to utter.
And even farther north,
Beyond the Firth of Forth,
The cuckoo tunes his note to Caledonian ears
And brings the rugged Scot to tears.

Ah, lucky men and happy counties these!
This year he did not come to us.
And now the days are long,
And the willow weeps for lack of song.

Has Highgate ceased to please?
Or, Cuckoo, did your little engine fail,
Breasting a gale
Over the narrow seas?

Anthony Washes

Anthony washed his face today –
  Nobody made him do it:
He wasn't told in the usual way;
  Nobody helped him through it.

He smiled his usual smile before,
  And teased his little sister;
Rose, but stopped on his way to the door;
  Thought a moment, and kissed her;

Turned and went of his own accord,
  With a stern but high demeanour;
And came back looking a trifle bored –
  But more than a trifle cleaner.

Anthony, Anthony, are you ill?
  Or is my eyesight failing?
You've washed your face of
    your own free will –
  Anthony, are you ailing?

The Hippopotamus's Birthday

He has opened all his parcels but the largest and the last;
His hopes are at their highest and his heart is beating
    fast.

O happy Hippopotamus, what lovely gift is here?
He cuts the string. The world stands still. A pair of
    boots appear!

O little Hippopotamus, the sorrows of the small!
He dropped two tears to mingle with the flowing
    Senegal;
And the 'Thank you' that he uttered was the saddest
    ever heard
In the Senegambian jungle from the mouth of beast or
    bird.

Mr Blob

My heart went out to Mr Blob the moment that we met,
And the manner of his coming is a thing I can't forget.
It fell upon a Sunday in the merry month of June,
Between a rainy morning and a rainy afternoon.

He didn't use the window, and he didn't use the door;
He never took his hat off, and he never touched the
    floor;
He didn't look as if he'd grown, like us: he just began,
And stood before us there, a simple English gentleman.

He wasn't very dandified or dainty in his dress,
But the absence of his trousers seemed to cause him no
    distress,
For the smile upon his features was a marvel to behold,
And underneath that buttoned vest there beat a heart of
    gold.

He wasn't long among us: all too little had been said
When a heavy hand descended on his inoffensive head,
And a Voice delivered judgment: 'Mr Blob is far too
    stout;
He's a silly little fellow, and I mean to rub him out.'

He didn't seem offended, but I think he must have
    heard,
For he rose up from the paper and he went without
    a word.
His boots and buttons only lingered on a little while,
And the last of him to vanish was the vestige of a smile.

O Mr Blob, the world would be a very pleasant place
If everyone resembled you in figure and in face.
If everybody went about with open arms like you
The stars would all be brighter and the sky a bluer blue.

My heart went out to Mr Blob the moment that we met,
And the sorrow of his going is a thing that haunts me
    yet;
For often when the clouds are low I sit at home and sob
To think that I shall see no more the face of Mr Blob.

Spring Song
For Two Voices

Spring came late.
But she came with a flourish; she came in a spate,
Bursting deliciously,
Subsurrepticiously,
Out of the snows of her winter repose.

One short night –
And the garden was bright, at a single bound,
With glamour and clamour and odour and sound;
The shrubs and the trees and the flowers were
shouting
(I meant to say shooting:
An owl did the hooting),
Cabbages sprouting, everything outing;
And in all the confusion of happy illusion
The perfumed song of a sweet-scented bird
Was inaudibly heard
Over the whistles of premature thistles,
And colourful capers
Of little boys gaily delivering papers.

CANTICLE TWO

One short night?
But you're talking absurdities,
Mixing your words. It is
Stupid to speak of a sweet-scented bird. It is
Sillier still to dwell on the thrill
Of hearing a whistle
From a caper-delivering papering lad —
Or was it a thistle?
You're driving me mad;
All that you state of the Spring that was late
Is quite indefensible.
Try to be sensible!

Me to be sensible?
Mind your own business!
Only a fool is at pains to be sensible
When all that he sees is incomprehensible.
The Spring I describe was light-headed herself,
A mystified elf,
Frenzied to dizziness
By the flap and the hurry, the worry and flurry
Of doing her duty and scattering beauty
Over the garden
In one short night.
So listen to me; for, begging your pardon,
It's you that are crazed
When you hint that my statements are faultily
phrased.

CANTICLE FOUR

The talented bird to whom I referred
In Canticle One,
And who acts as conductor and singing instructor
To his cousins and brothers and dozens of others,
Had scarcely concluded his hymn to the dawn
When, observing the sun,
He threw down his baton and putting his hat on
Led all his young choristers on to the lawn,

Where he showed them, by hopping
But now and then stopping and cocking an eye,
How to descry
The longest and juiciest bits in the pie.
This done,
The innocent dears,

Leaving the worm population in tears,
  Came to the door,
And knocking repeatedly asked me for more –
Asked me for bedding, asked me for mats
To furnish their new, commodious flats,
Stressing their hopes of enriching our lives
With the aid of their sky-born impeccable wives.
  What could I say,
  In view of the day?
What could I do but show them the way
  To my elegant roses,
Saying, 'On those is the flannel and twine
I have hitherto fondly regarded as mine'?
And so after pecking and wrecking the bands
They left me, with mutual shaking of hands.

And a hedgehog appeared . . . .
A hedgehog in Spring?
What a wonderful thing!
Did you dial his number and give him a ring?
This is worse than I feared!
Are you going to say
That a hedgehog is something out of the way,
And not, as Biology stoutly maintains,
A dull little mammal without any brains?

I repeat, in spite of your interpolation,
He came – in a mood of subdued exaltation,
Deigning to grace the approach to our portals
That serves as a rule for nothing but mortals.
Ah what do I care,
With Spring in the air,
For the learned and ignorant works of those
Who write of the hedgehog in ponderous prose?
I sing him in verse;
I sing of the length of his sensitive nose,
Of the way that he rose
And ran on his toes;
Of his spherical form with its jacket of thistles
(Delete the word 'thistles' and substitute 'bristles');
And I add to all that
That when kissed by the cat

He withdrew to the scene of his long hibernation
With the air of a saint in sublime meditation.

CANTICLE SIX

No, I never have seen and there never has been
    A Spring so green,
So quick and serene, so ineffably clean.
    Do you see what I mean?
    To a certain degree –
Through the murk and the haze of your paean of praise
    I admit that I see
    (My relief is immense!)
A faint and occasional glimmer of sense.
    Then let us unite
    And prepare to indite
A novel Biology, different quite
From the sort that the standard authorities write.
We will learn to commune with my clerical friend
(I should have said 'spherical' – kindly emend)
    Over the phone,
On a private celestial line of our own;
We will soar on the wings of my sweet-scented bird
    To the realms of delight
Where fancy is truth, and facts are absurd;
For if we could capture the surge and the urge
    Of the Spring that was late,
Ah what a book, what a world would emerge!

The Lady of Leigh

'Misery me!'
  Said the Lady of Leigh,
As she queued for a bus in the Strand,
And callous conductresses, weary of work,
Drifted disdainfully into the murk
  With a laugh at her lily-white hand.
'Oh the ladylike ease at Leigh on the Sea!
The curtains and comfort, the toast and the tea!
There goes another one – misery me!
  Misery me!'
  Said the Lady of Leigh.

Night Thought

Oh, what's the good of staying up and yawning
And using up the artificial light?
For anything may happen in the morning,
And nothing ever happens in the night.

Decline and Fall

'The Decline and Fall of the Empire of Rome'
Is a book that my daughter is reading at home,
Not entirely for fun, nor indeed for a bet:
It's the book that her brutal examiners set.

Now who was the man who faced up to the work
And told the whole tale from the start to the Turk?
Until I adjusted my type-writer ribbon,
I *could* not remember. Ah yes! It was Gibbon.

Mumfludgeons

So they camped upon the common in the gloaming of the
    day,
And cooked themselves mumfludgeons in the ancient
    Cornish way.
'The wind may blow, the tent may go,' their bearded
    leader said;
'But he who eats mumfludgeons goes ballasted to bed.

'And oh, what rich perfumes are these that waft me to
    Peru?
Is this the wine of Mexico, the *chocolatl* true?
Lift high your chin! Tilt up the tin! Who fills himself
    with such
Shall sleep as Montezuma slept, and dream – not
    overmuch.'

They supped in simple-hearted glee, as pampered people
    dine;
They smoked the pipe of Paradise, and quaffed the Aztec
    wine.
What if the tempest raged without, and all within was
    moist?
They gloried in their bearded chief; and he in them
    rejoiced.

The Author

What kind of a man made this poetry scan?
　　Is he wholly and utterly bad?
Does he ever have gleams, in his happier dreams,
　　Of himself as an innocent lad?
Will he do it again? Could we lessen his pain
　　With the aid of medicinal herbs?
Though I'd rather retort with a sneeze or a snort,
　　I will answer in regular verbs.

If you speak to him fast, or refer to his past,
　　Or allude to the National Debt,
He takes on a look like the back of a book
　　Or a house with a notice To Let.
If you ask him a riddle, or hand him a fiddle,
　　He moves to a quieter place;
But he's easily led to stay out of his bed
　　And explain Four-Dimensional Space.

Every day of the week with his tongue in his cheek
　　He goes to an office to work.
If they bring him a file he replies with a smile
　　And passes it on to a clerk.
When addressing his chief he is polished and brief;
　　He is charming to ladies who call –
To the rest his remarks are a series of barks,
　　Or else he says nothing at all.

In the home that he loves, though he never wears gloves,
　　His manners are better than *that*:
He flatters his cook with a gratified look;
　　He opens the door for the cat.
And if, when he's told to turn over the mould,
　　He refuses in musical verse,
Such as 'Begging your pardon, I won't dig the garden,'
　　Does that make it better or worse?

But oh, what a life for his ladylike wife
　　With her elegant daughters and sons!
For when threatened with rain or missing a train
　　He not only rhymes but he puns;
And he laughs till he chokes at his own little jokes
　　And expects other people to try –
Her hair has grown grey in attempts to obey
　　And her smile has been twisted awry.

I could write, had I space, of his beautiful face,
　　Of his wisdom, good temper, and tact;
How from earliest youth he has worshipped the truth
　　And never distorted a fact.
I could make you say: 'Oh, how delightful to know
　　That his eyes are forget-me-not blue!'
I could weave you a story of goodness and glory –
　　I could: but it wouldn't be true.

End of Volume One?

The golden days are over –
  The laughter and the pain.
The wild flowers and the roses,
  They will not bloom again.

Yet they had hardly opened
  Their petals to the sun
Before the mist began to creep
  And the golden days were done.